RVers GAG GUIDE TO CAMPS, RANTS AND RIGS

OR

RVers COLLECTION OF CARTOON CAMPING CAPERS

Created and Illustrated by
Gilbert W. Davies

Lettering by
Florice M. Frank

HiStory ink Books
PO Box 52
Hat Creek, California 96040

Contents

1

2

3

THE HAVE AND HAVE NOT AGENCIES

5

SALES PITCH

8

9

NEW PRIORITIES

13

14

15

CAMPGROUND RATES

A	NO HOOKUPS	$12
B	ELECTRICITY ONLY	$13
C	WATER ONLY	$14
D	SEWER ONLY	$15
E	ELECTRICITY & WATER ONLY	$16
F	WATER & SEWER ONLY	$17
G	SEWER & ELECTRICITY	$18
H	WATER, SEWER & ELECTRICITY ONLY	$19
I	WITH PET (DOG, CAT, FISH, BIRD or RODENT)	$5
J	TWO OR MORE PETS EACH	$1
K	CHILDREN (SEE RATES FOR PETS ABOVE)	
L	SENIORS (SINCE YOU NOW HAVE $$$--) ADD	$4
M	CABLE HOOKUP	$1
N	COMPUTER HOOKUP	$2
O	PHONE HOOKUP	$3

WEEKLY RATES:

WITH A ABOVE	DEDUCT	5%
WITH B, C OR D	DEDUCT	8%
WITH E, F OR G	DEDUCT	10%
WITH H	DEDUCT	11%
WITH I, J, K OR L	DEDUCT	3%
WITH M AND/OR N (COUCH POTATO TAX)		20%+

NOTE: WE NEED AT LEAST THREE HOURS
             NOTICE TO COMPUTE YOUR PAYMENT

17

RVers DECIDING TEAMS FOR BALL GAME

SALES PITCH

MOTORHOME MOM

COLD COUNTRY RV LIVING

ALI BABA AND HIS DUTCH DOOR TRAILER HOME

25

26

27

29

30

RESULTS OF A BUSTED BUBBLE

JACK! DID YOU CHECK TO LOCK THE DOOR, THE VENTS, THE AWNING, THE WINDOWS, THE HOT WATER HEATER, THE CURTAINS, OUTSIDE LIGHTS, THE DRIPPING FAUCET, THE DOG'S WATER DISH, TOMORROW'S WEATHER AND SET THE ALARM?
ZZZZZ

34

GOOD TIMES CAMPGROUND

A FEW RULES

NO FIRES   NO FISHING   NO SWIMMING

NO LITTERING   NO RUNNING   NO PETS

NO SMOKING   NO BICYCLES   NO LOITERING

NO HORSES   NO GENERATORS   NO ALCOHOL

NO WHISTLING   NO PARTYING   NO YELLING

NO SPITTING   NO SWEARING   NO BALL PLAY

NO WHOOPIE   NO NONSENSE   NO QUESTIONS

ENJOY YOUR STAY

36

37

38

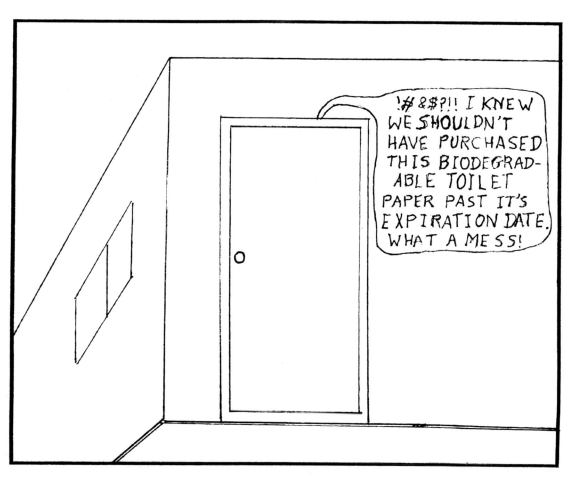

39

40

41

DIRT ROAD DRIVING

45

46

47

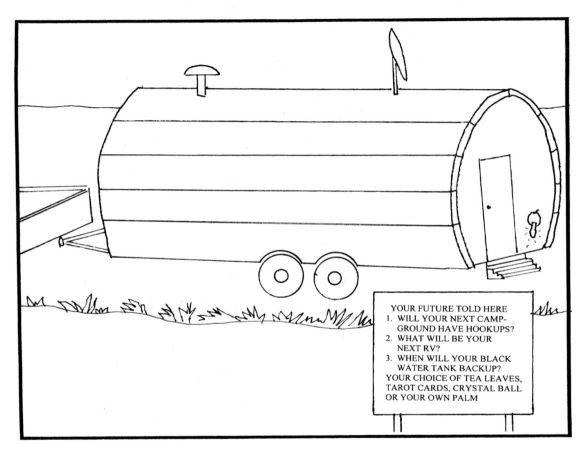

YOUR FUTURE TOLD HERE
1. WILL YOUR NEXT CAMP-
   GROUND HAVE HOOKUPS?
2. WHAT WILL BE YOUR
   NEXT RV?
3. WHEN WILL YOUR BLACK
   WATER TANK BACKUP?
YOUR CHOICE OF TEA LEAVES,
TAROT CARDS, CRYSTAL BALL
OR YOUR OWN PALM

GYPSY RVer

SALES PITCH

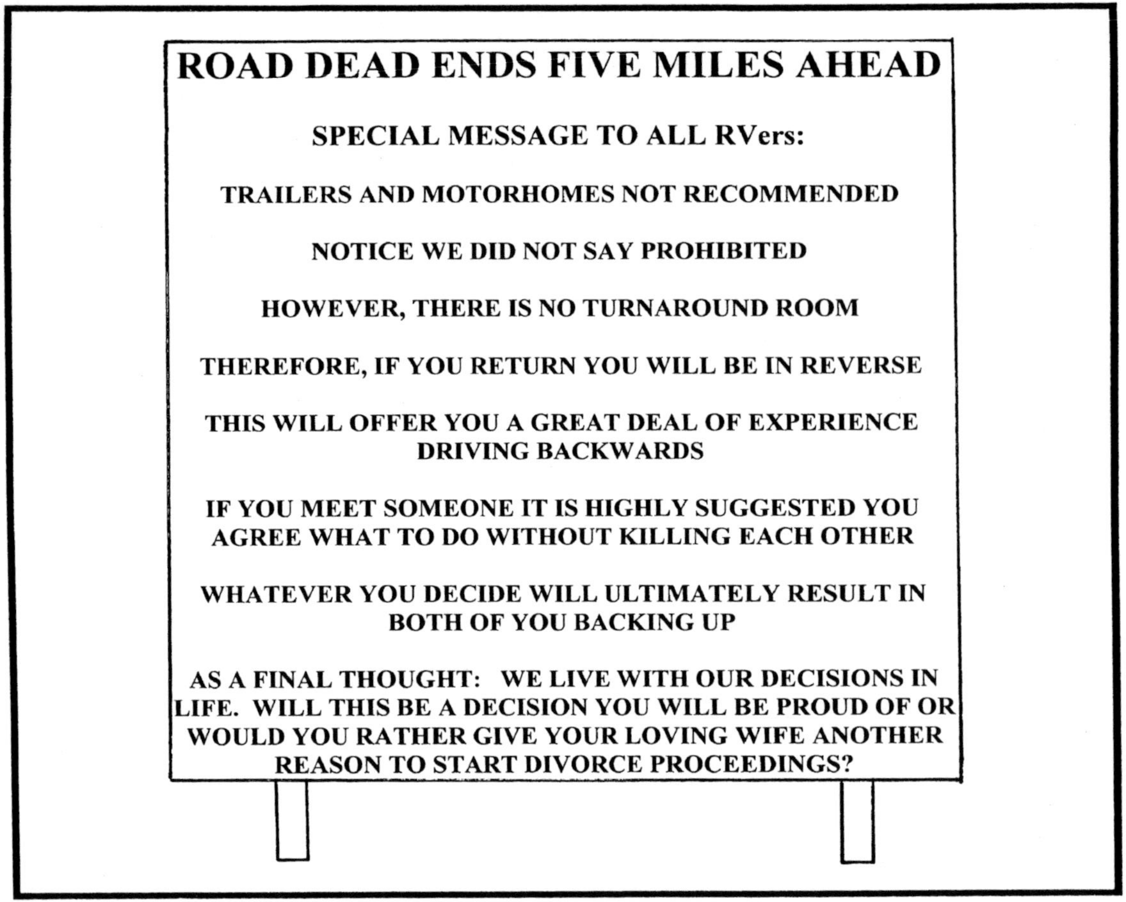

ROAD DEAD ENDS FIVE MILES AHEAD

SPECIAL MESSAGE TO ALL RVers:

TRAILERS AND MOTORHOMES NOT RECOMMENDED

NOTICE WE DID NOT SAY PROHIBITED

HOWEVER, THERE IS NO TURNAROUND ROOM

THEREFORE, IF YOU RETURN YOU WILL BE IN REVERSE

**THIS WILL OFFER YOU A GREAT DEAL OF EXPERIENCE
DRIVING BACKWARDS**

**IF YOU MEET SOMEONE IT IS HIGHLY SUGGESTED YOU
AGREE WHAT TO DO WITHOUT KILLING EACH OTHER**

**WHATEVER YOU DECIDE WILL ULTIMATELY RESULT IN
BOTH OF YOU BACKING UP**

**AS A FINAL THOUGHT: WE LIVE WITH OUR DECISIONS IN
LIFE. WILL THIS BE A DECISION YOU WILL BE PROUD OF OR
WOULD YOU RATHER GIVE YOUR LOVING WIFE ANOTHER
REASON TO START DIVORCE PROCEEDINGS?**

50

52

53

54

CHIROPRACTOR'S OFFICE

UNDERCOVER CAMPGROUND INSPECTORS

MODERN VACATION

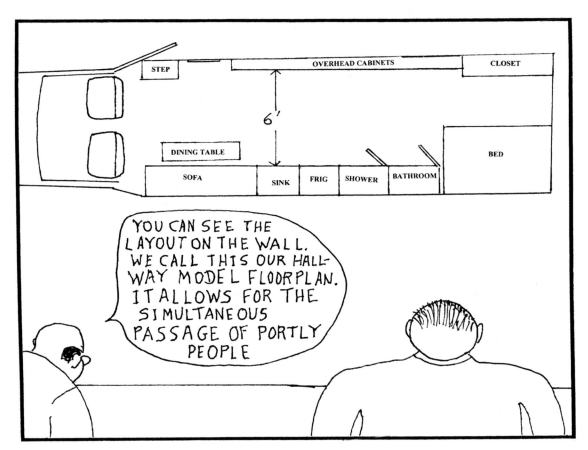

SALES PITCH

FIRST TIME FILL-UP

63

65

A HORSE IS A HORSE, OF COURSE

SALES PITCH

HELPFUL NEIGHBORS

73

74   HONEYMOONERS ABOUT TO HAVE THEIR FIRST ARGUMENT

SALES PITCH

FULL TIMERS

SALES PITCH

KNOCK! KNOCK!

SALES PITCH

81

83

DISH DRAG

STYLE POINTS FOR BACKING INTO SITE

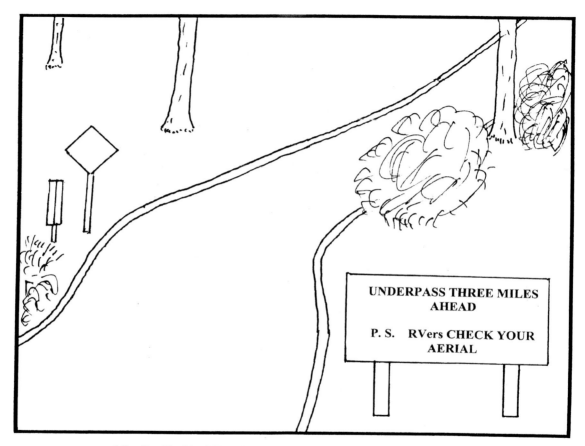

UNDERPASS THREE MILES
AHEAD

P. S.   RVers CHECK YOUR
AERIAL

COURTESY OF AN RVing HIGHWAY ENGINEER

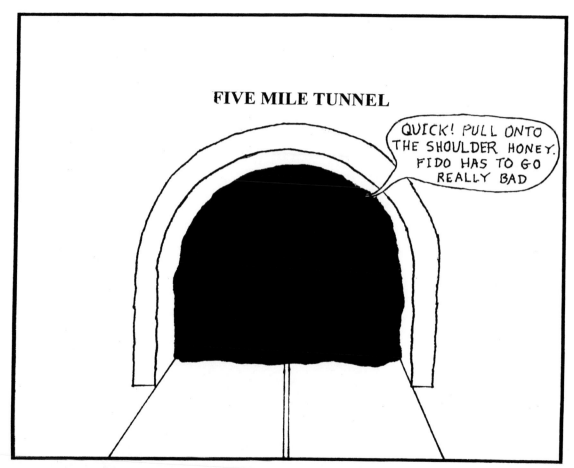

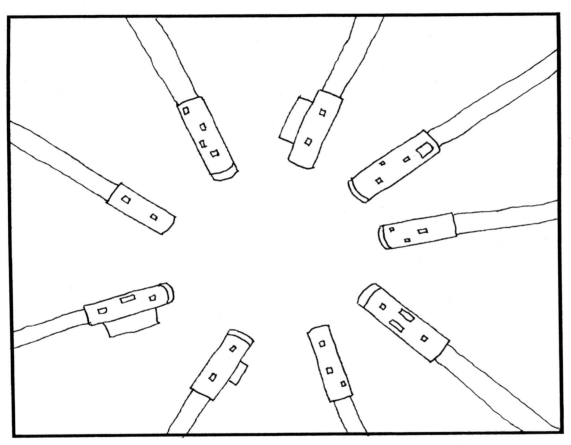

RAILROAD RETIREE'S ROUNDHOUSE RALLY

91

92

93

94

96

98